BASTIEN PIANO BASIC
TECHNIC
PRIMER LEVEL
BY JAMES BASTIEN

Contents

*To reinforce the feeling of achievement, the teacher or student may put a √ when the page has been mastered.

ISBN 0-8497-5280-9

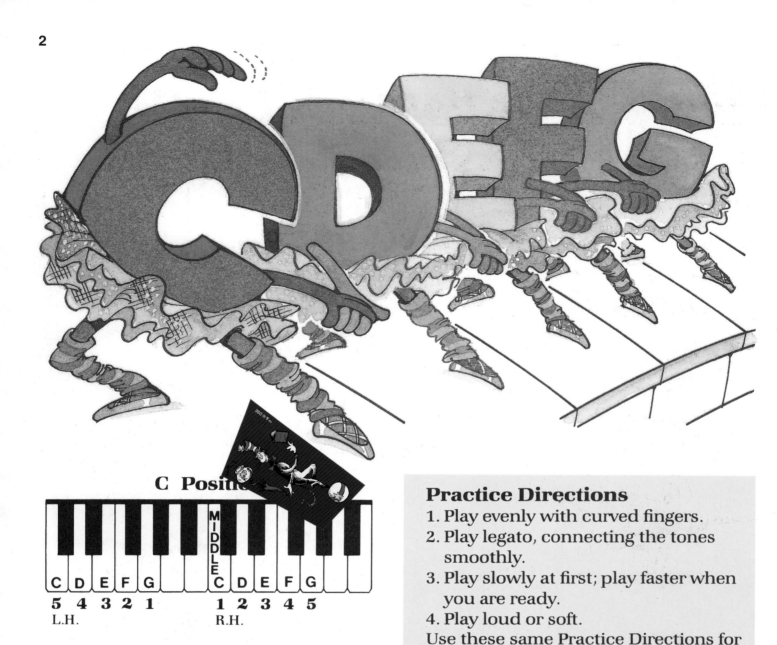

C Position

Practice Directions
1. Play evenly with curved fingers.
2. Play legato, connecting the tones smoothly.
3. Play slowly at first; play faster when you are ready.
4. Play loud or soft.

Use these same Practice Directions for pages 3-5.

C Warm-up

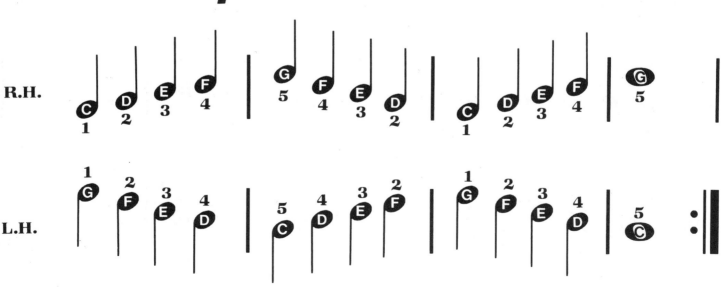

Climbing the Bars

Teeter-Totter Fun!

4

Sea Whale

Ocean Octopus

Use with pages 18-23 of Piano, Primer Level.

The Merry-Go-Round

Circus Clown

C Position

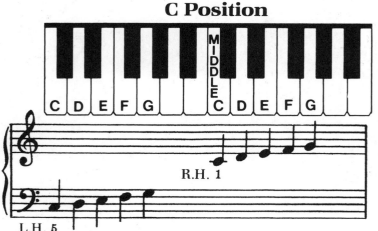

f-p means to play the first time *f* (loud), the second time *p* (so...

Roller Coaster Ride

Play hands separately first.
Repeat and play hands together.*

On the Ferris Wheel

*Teacher: This practice direction is only a suggestion. You may want the student to begin with both hands.

Monkey Twins

Three Giraffes

Lift your hand at the end of each slur with an "up wrist" motion. Lift on count 3.

Floating Clouds

lift hand   lift hand

Lift your hand at the end of each slur with an "up wrist" motion. Lift on count 4.

Lifting Balloons

lift hand

lift hand

Observe the ties.
Lift your hand at the end
of each slur on count 4.

Tied Score

f - p

Observe the ties.
Lift your hands at the end
of each slur on count 3.

All Tied Up!

f - p

Four Crows

Five Rabbits

Melodic Intervals

Harmonic Intervals

After playing each interval twice as written, you may then repeat each interval three times, then four times.

Clip-Clop Trail

Echo Canyon

Chords Are Fun!

f-p Play this chord, | C's its name, | Curve your fin-gers, | please take aim!

*Continue this pattern up the keyboard on the white keys.

In each exercise below, play the chords softer than the melody.

Melody and Chords

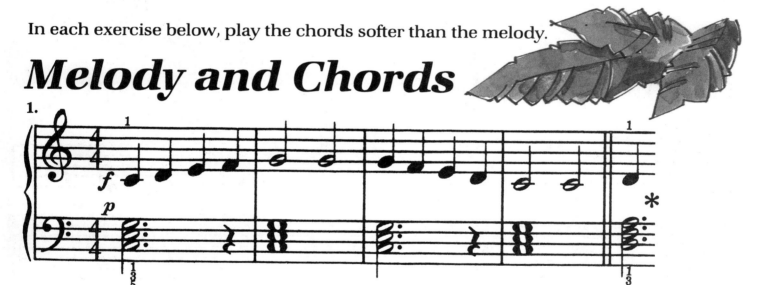

1.

*Continue this pattern up the keyboard on the white keys.

2.

*Continue this pattern up the keyboard on the white keys.

Harp Chords

*Continue this pattern up the keyboard on the white keys.

Middle C Position

Let's Go Sliding!

*Continue this pattern up the keyboard on the white keys.

Bees in Springtime

*Continue this pattern up the keyboard on the white keys.

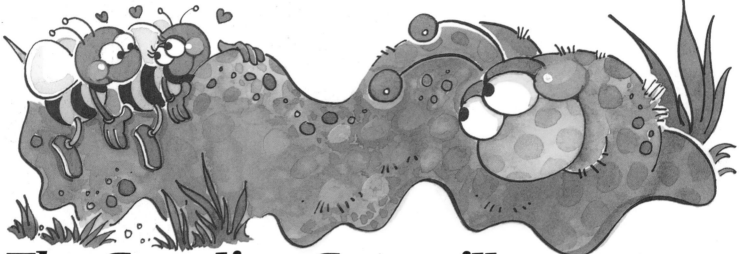

The Crawling Caterpillar

*Continue this pattern up the keyboard on the white keys.

Use with page 46-47 of Piano, *Primer Level.* **WP215**

Hear the Wind Blow!

Use with pages 48-49 of Piano, *Primer Level.*

The Busy Windmill

G Position

2nds and 3rds

Hopscotch

G Chords

Boogie Time

Let's Jump!

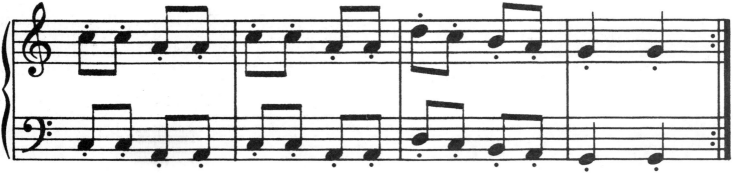

Bouncing Balls

Wooden Shoe Dance

Use with page 57 of Piano, Primer Level. **WP215**

In Outer Space

Robot Companions

Let's Rock!

28

Begin with a low wrist, and end with a
high wrist for each slurred group.

Phrasing 2's

*Continue this pattern up the keyboard on the white keys.

Phrasing 3's

*Continue this pattern up the keyboard on the white keys.

Indian Brave

Special Requests for Technic